Smooth Jazz Piano Solos

This publication is not authorised for sale in the
United States of America and/or Canada.

Wise Publications
London/New York/Paris/Sydney/Copenhagen/Madrid/Tokyo

Exclusive distributors:
Music Sales Limited, 8/9 Frith Street, London W1D 3JB, England.
Music Sales Pty Limited, 120 Rothschild Avenue, Rosebery, NSW 2018, Australia.

Order No. AM967956
ISBN 0-7119-8554-5
This book © Copyright 1997, 2000 by Wise Publications
(Previously published as Jazz Cafe for Solo Piano)

Compiled by Peter Evans
Music arranged by Jack Long
Music processed by Enigma Music Production Services
Cover design by Chloë Alexander
Printed in the United Kingdom

Your Guarantee of Quality
As publishers, we strive to produce every book to the highest commercial standards.
This the book has been carefully designed to minimise awkward page turns and to
make playing from it a real pleasure.
Particular care has been given to specifying acid-free, neutral-sized paper made from
pulps which have not been elemental chlorine bleached. This pulp is from farmed
sustainable forests and was produced with special regard for the environment.
Throughout, the printing and binding have been planned to ensure a sturdy, attractive
publication which should give years of enjoyment. If your copy fails to meet our high
standards, please inform us and we will gladly replace it.

Music Sales' complete catalogue describes thousands of titles and is available in full
colour sections by subject, direct from Music Sales Limited. Please state your areas of
interest and send a cheque/postal order for £1.50 for postage to: Music Sales Limited,
Newmarket Road, Bury St. Edmunds, Suffolk IP33 3YB.

www.musicsales.com

CONTENTS

9 95

Fly Me To The Moon (In Other Words)

Words & Music by Bart Howard

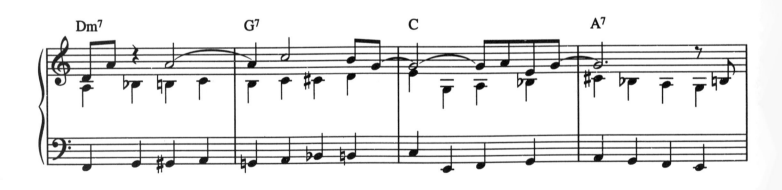

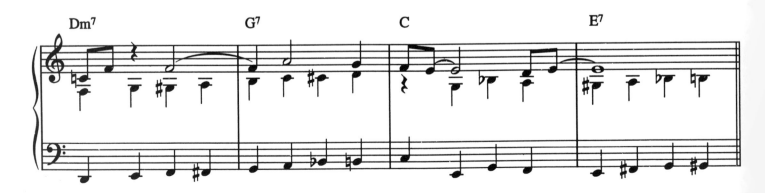

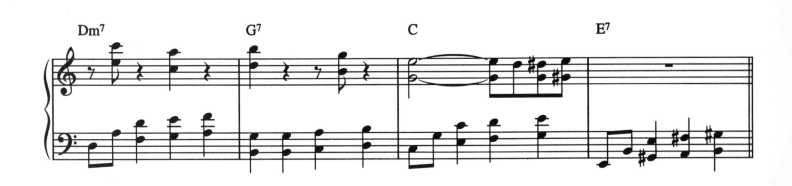

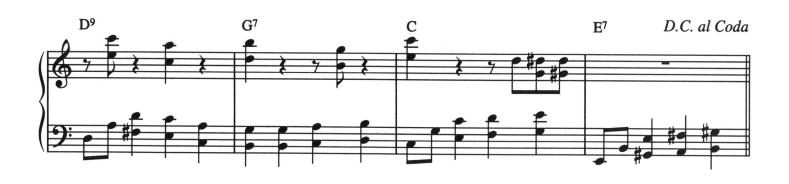

CODA

8va bassa

Chelsea Bridge

By Billy Strayhorn

Slow

Very freely, out of tempo

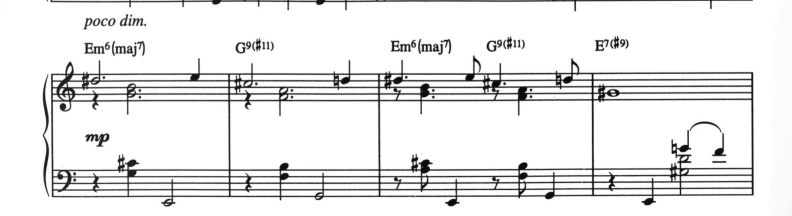

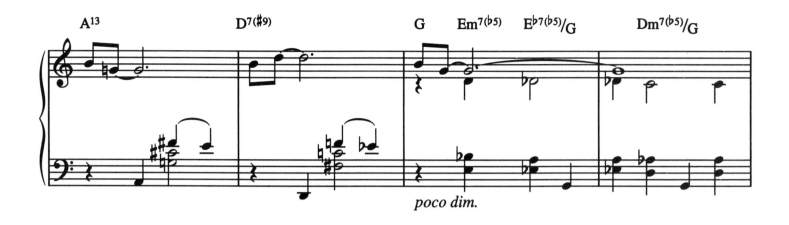

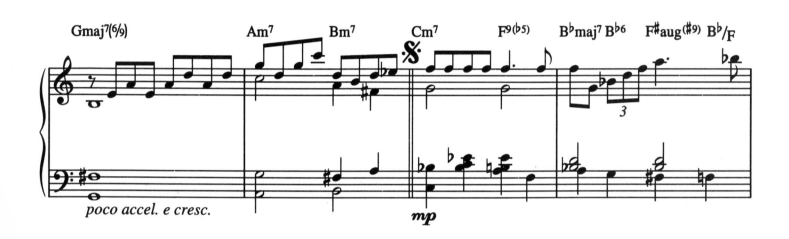

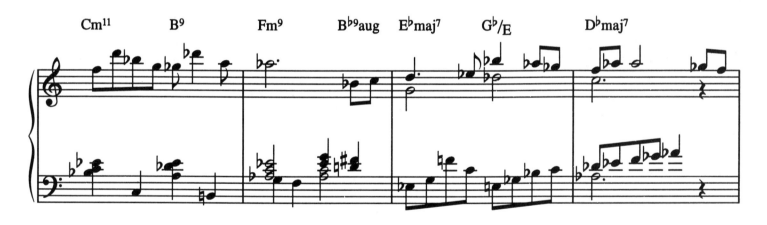

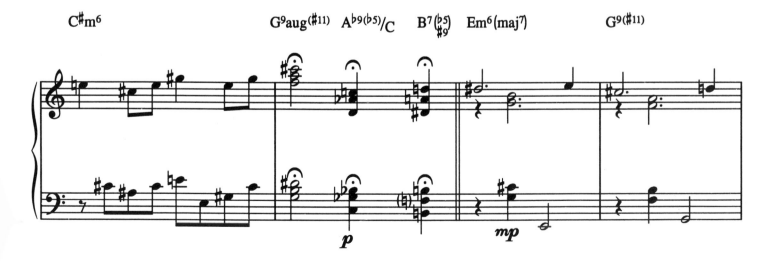

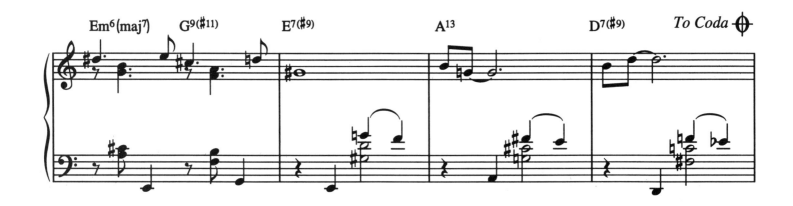

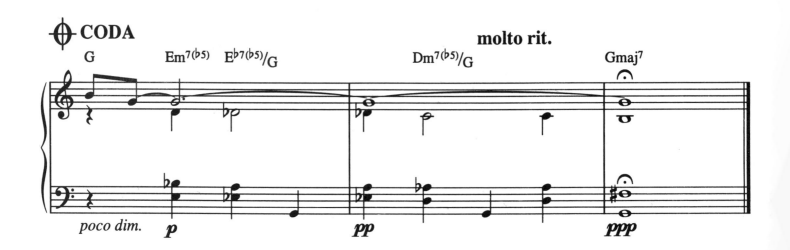

Honeysuckle Rose

Music by Thomas 'Fats' Waller
Words by Andy Razaf

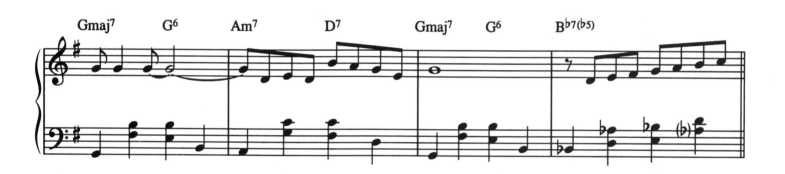

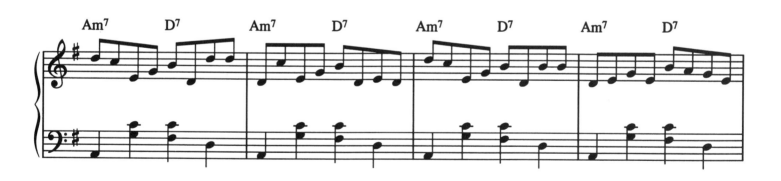

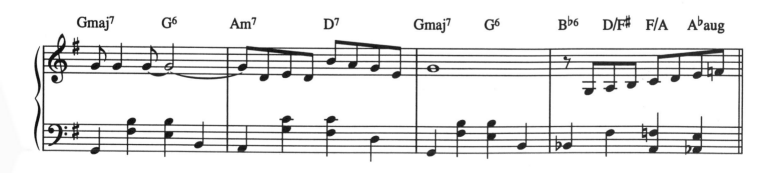

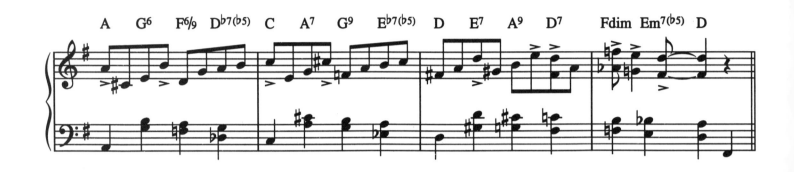

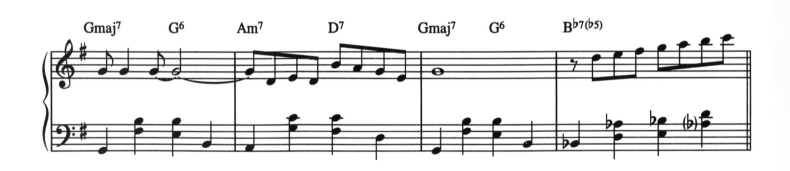

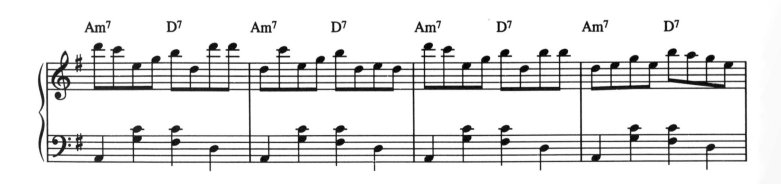

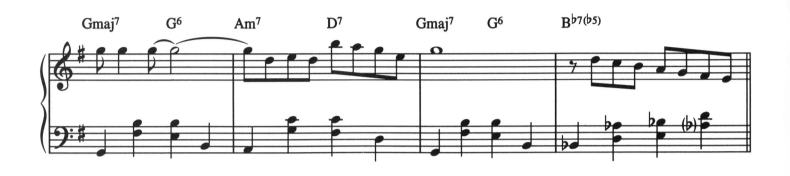

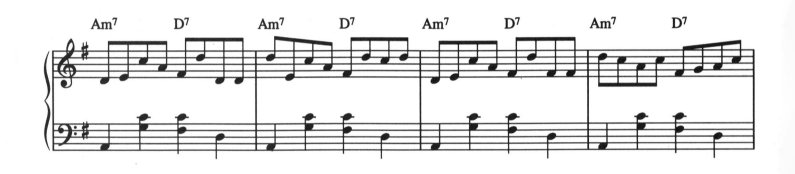

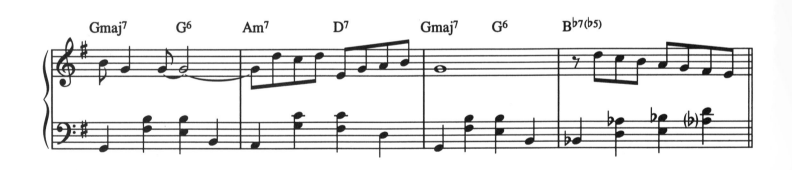

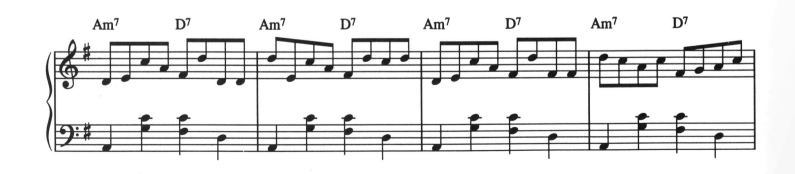

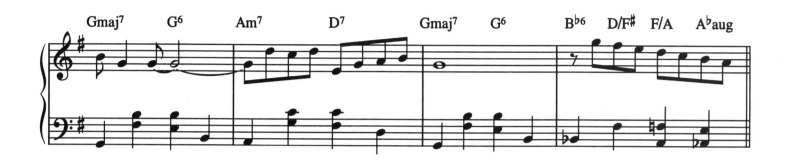

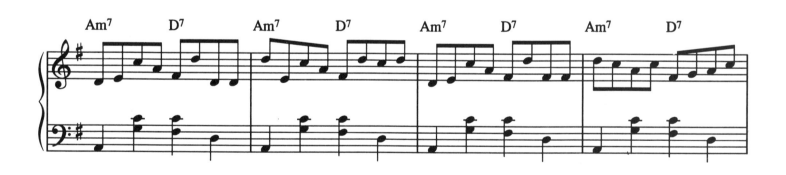

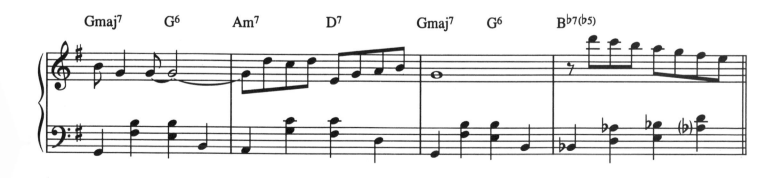

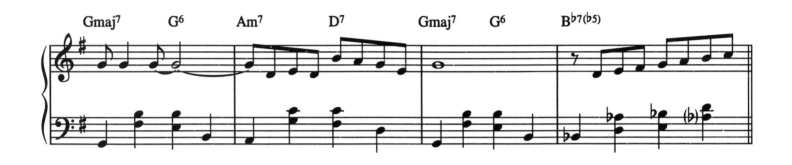

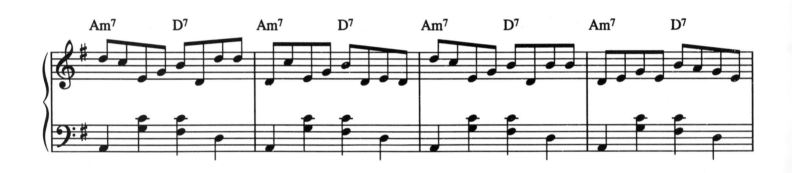

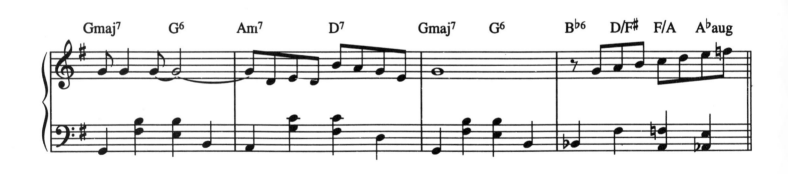

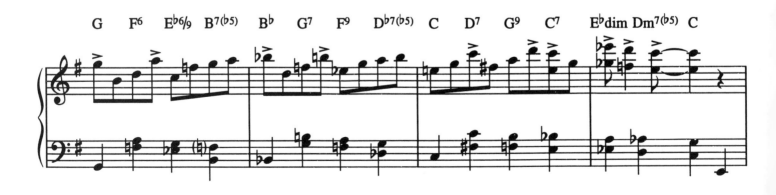

Here's That Rainy Day

Words & Music by Johnny Burke & Jimmy Van Heusen

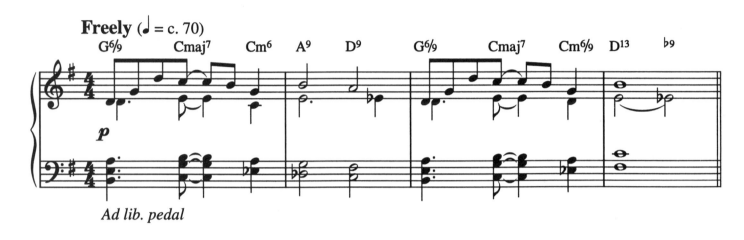

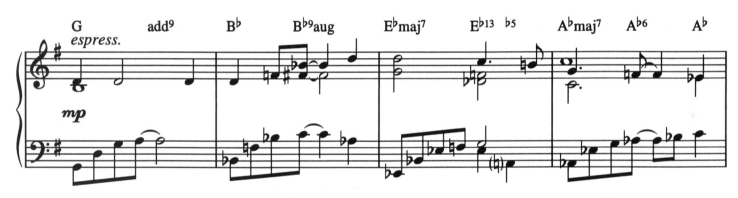

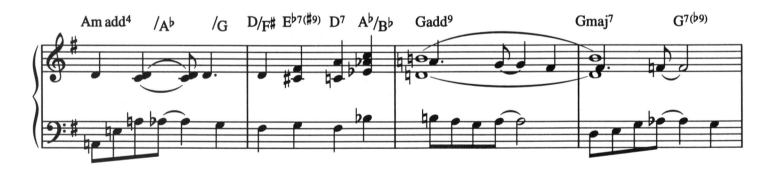

I Wanna Be Around

Words & Music by Johnny Mercer & Sadie Vimmerstedt

I'll Remember April

Words & Music by Don Raye, Gene de Paul & Patricia Johnson

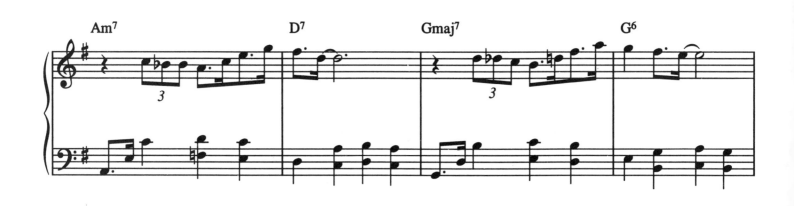

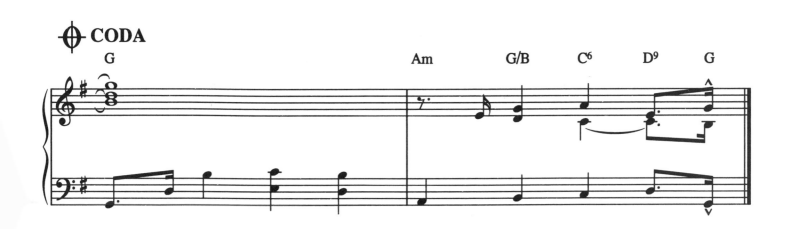

I'm Gettin' Sentimental Over You

Words by Ned Washington
Music by Geo. Bassman

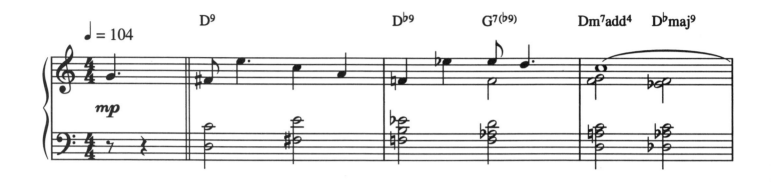

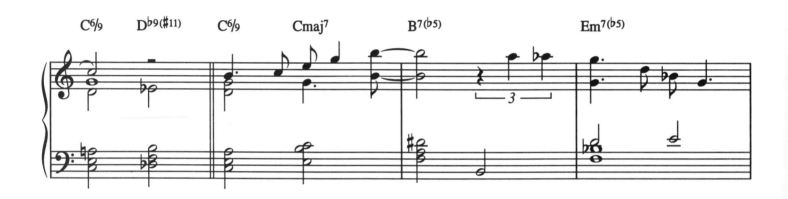

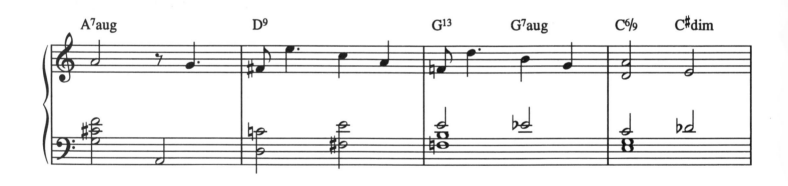

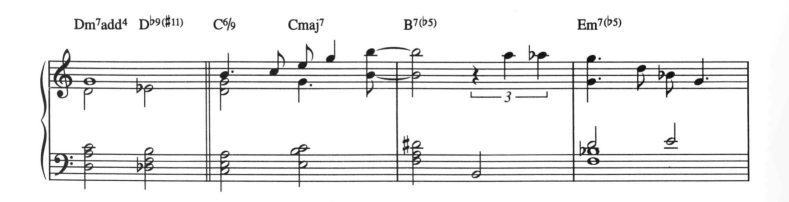

A little slower ($\quarternote = 90$), **but more rhythmically**

Lazy River

Words & Music by Hoagy Carmichael & Sidney Arodin

Recado Bossa Nova (The Gift)

Words & Music by Djalma Ferreira & Luiz Antonio

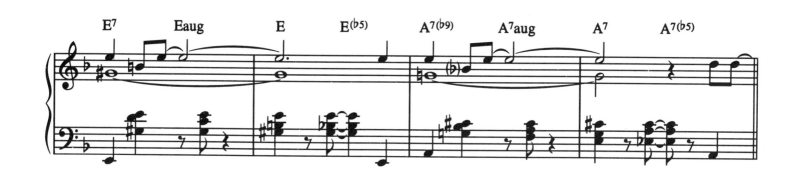

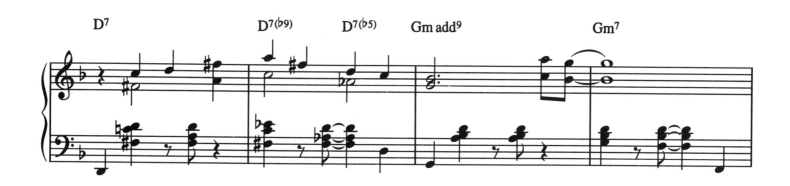

2nd time D. 𝄋 al Coda

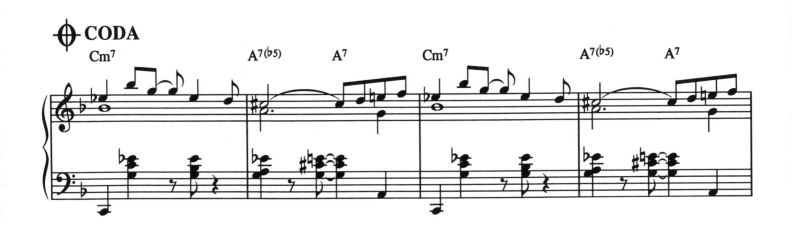

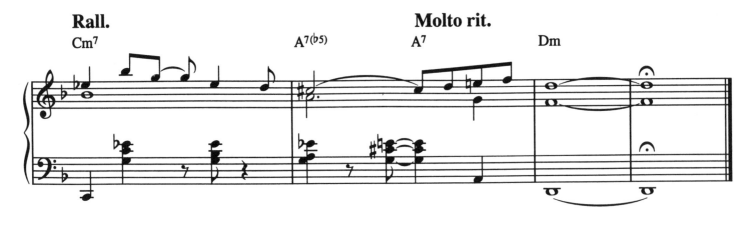

Satin Doll

Words by Johnny Mercer
Music by Duke Ellington & Billy Strayhorn

D. %̲ al Coda

Taking A Chance On Love

Words by John La Touche & Ted Fetter
Music by Vernon Duke

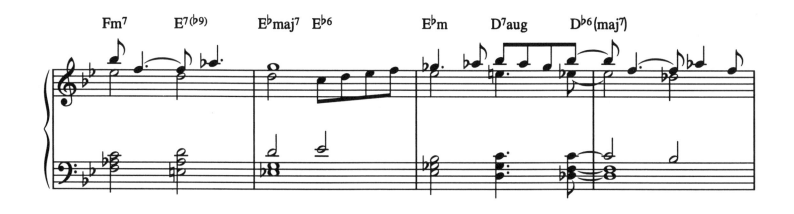

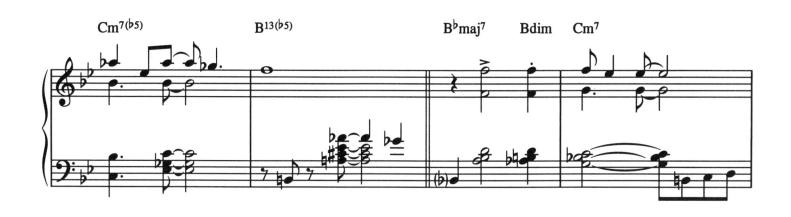

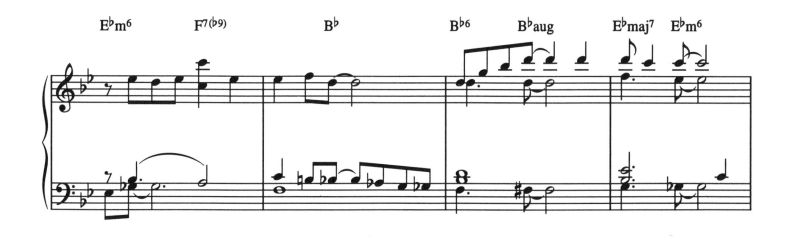

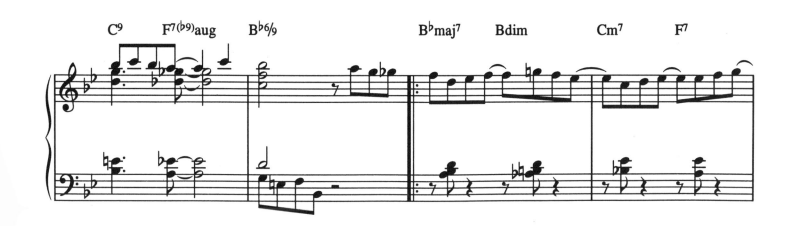

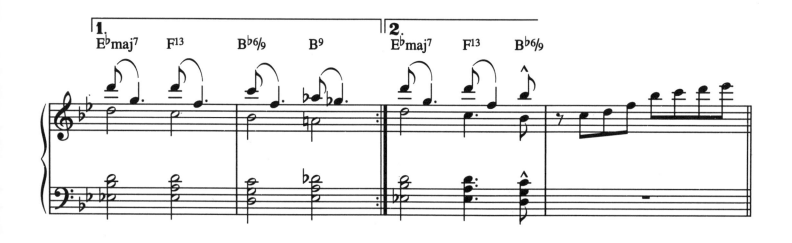

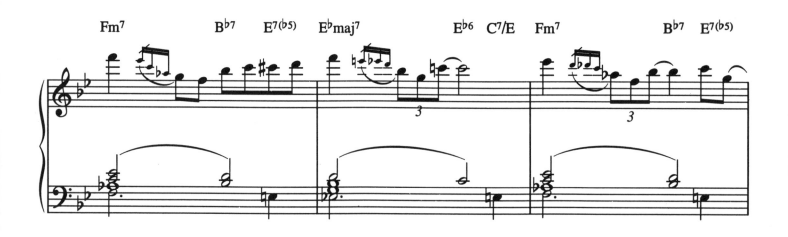

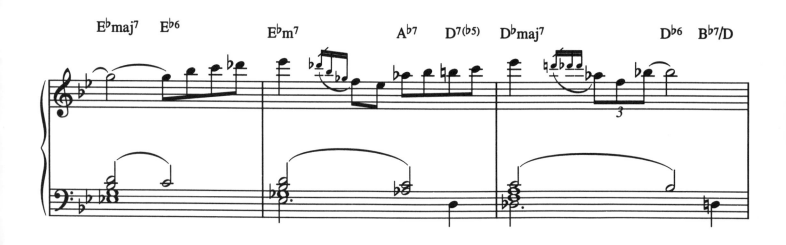

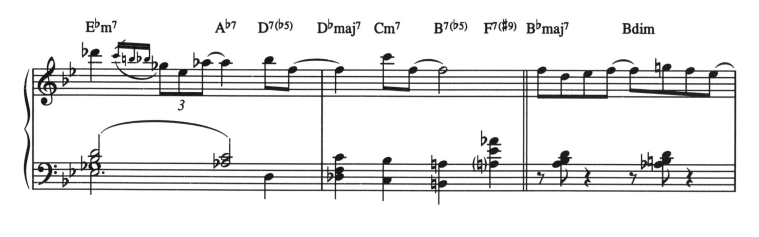

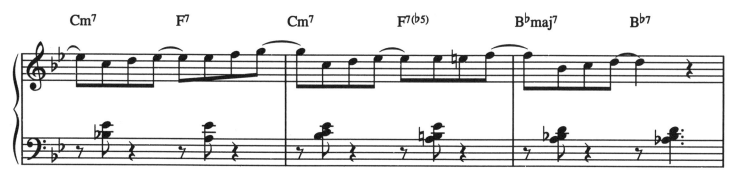

D.%$ (with repeats) al Coda

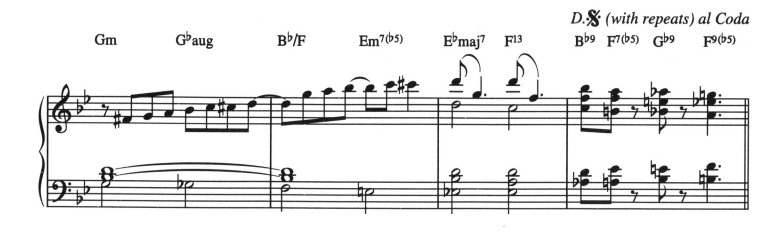

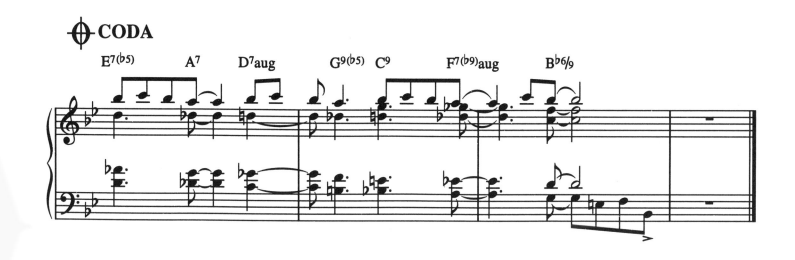

The Girl From Ipanema (Garota De Ipanema)

Original Words by Vinicius De Moraes
English Lyric by Norman Gimbel
Music by Antonio Carlos Jobim

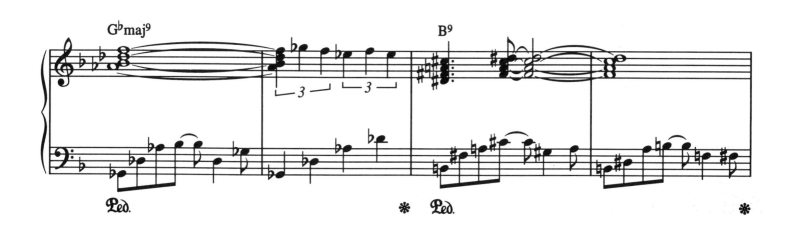

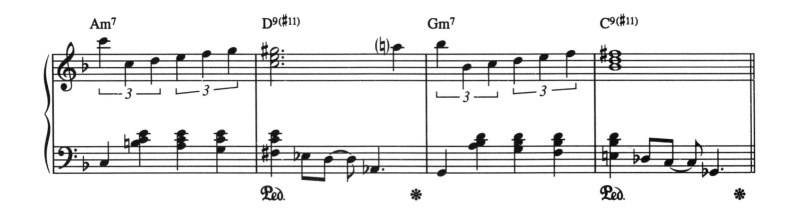

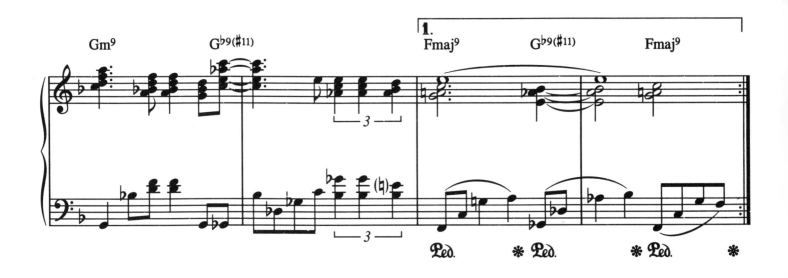

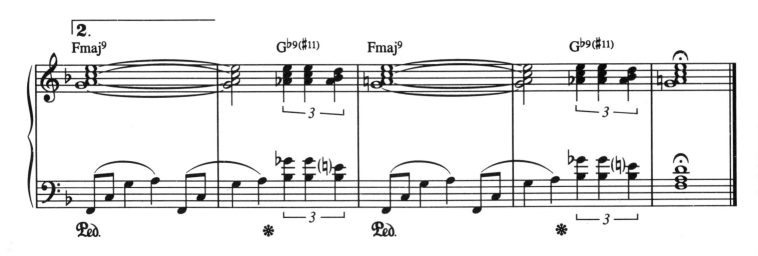

The Nearness Of You

Music by Hoagy Carmichael
Words by Ned Washington

Undecided

Words by Sid Robin
Music by Charles Shavers

To Coda ⊕

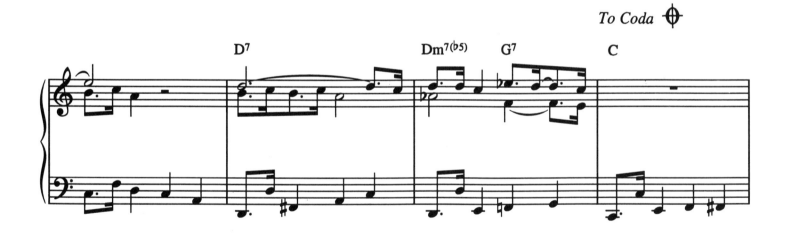

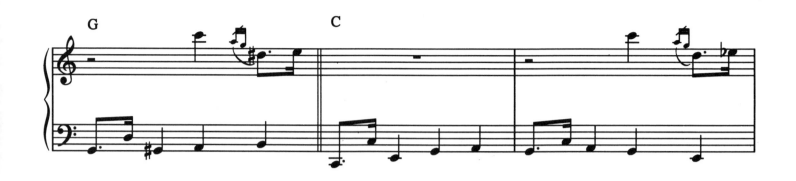

D.%: (with repeat) al Coda

CODA

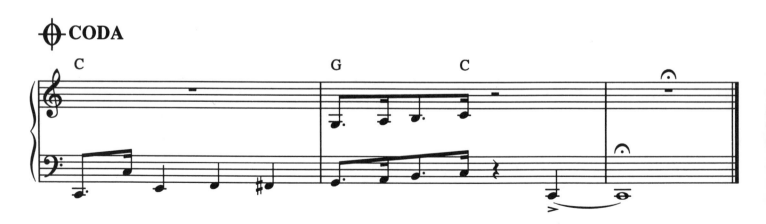

When Sunny Gets Blue

Words by Jack Segal
Music by Marvin Fisher

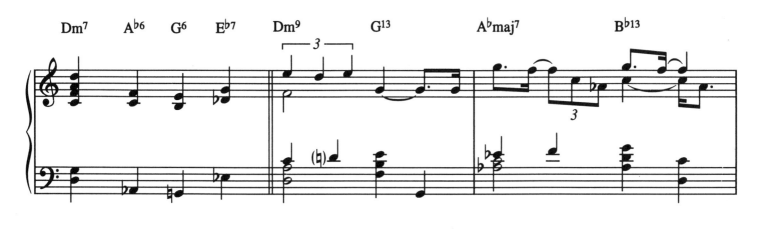

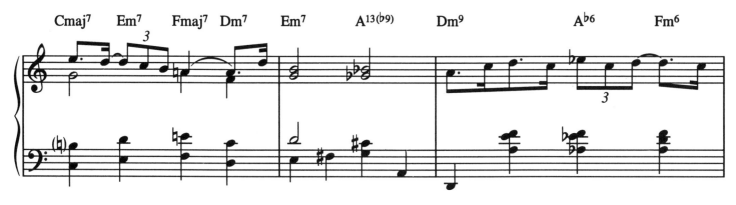

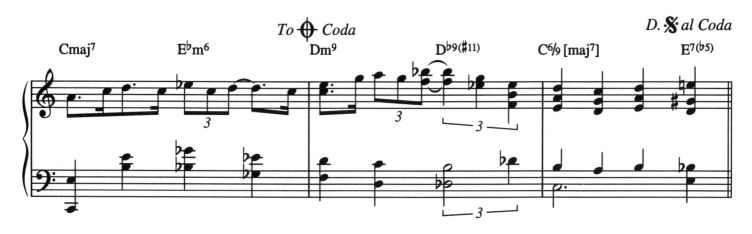

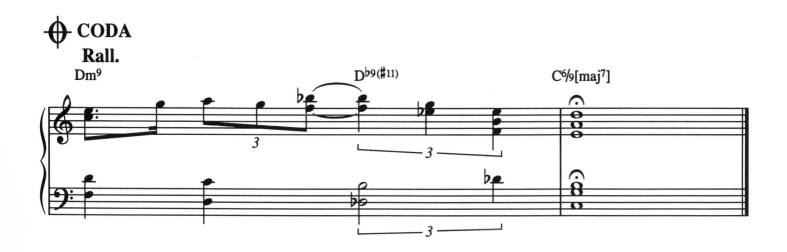